THE
NEW BARNES
READERS
— THE KEARNY PLAN —

HERMAN DRESSEL
Superintendent of Schools, Kearny, N. J.

MAY ROBBINS
Primary Superintendent, Kearny, N. J.

ELLIS U. GRAFF
Superintendent of Schools, Indianapolis

BOOK THREE

Illustrated by Mabel B. Hill

LAIDLAW BROTHERS
Publishers
Chicago   New York

Grateful acknowledgment is made for permission to use selections as follows
" *Trading Timothy Titus,*" *published by Youths Companion.*
" *The Brownies,*" *by Jane L. Hoxie, and* "*Persephone*" *by Carolyn S. Bailey,*
   published by Milton Bradley Co.
" *Making the Best of It,*" *by Frances Fox, published by The Outlook Co.*
" *The Little Brown Bowl,*" *by Phila Butler Bowman, published by The*
   Churchman Co.
" *Li'l' Hannibal,*" *by Carolyn S. Bailey, published by* "*Good Housekeeping*"
" *Wynken, Blynken, and Nod,*" *by Eugene Field, is used by permission of*
   and special arrangement with Charles Scribner's Sons.
" *The Oak Tree and the Linden*" *and* " *St. George and the Dragon,*" *by*
   Carolyn S. Bailey, are used by permission of and special arrangement
   with Milton Bradley Co.

CONTENTS

CONTENTS

THE MAGIC FLOWER

I

Switzerland is one of the most beautiful countries in the world. It has lofty mountains, fertile valleys, wonderful lakes, and beautiful streams that flash and foam as they rush down the mountains to the sea.

It is said that long ago the mountains of Switzerland were full of fairies; that the hills swarmed with dwarfs, elves, and gnomes.

In those days, on the side of one of the mountains, lived little Arnold and his mother. The father died when Arnold was a baby, and left the poor mother with only a little plot of land and a few goats.

When Arnold grew older, he faithfully guarded the goats on the mountain-side through the day, and when the sun set, he guided them home again.

He had no time to play, for in the evening the wood was to be cut, the goats milked, and the garden weeded.

When Arnold was about ten years old, his mother became very, very ill. An old woman who helped care for her, said, "There is only one thing that will cure your mother, Arnold. It is a little brown herb, that grows at the top of the mountain, but now the mountain is covered with ice and snow."

"I care not for ice and snow," said little Arnold. "If the herb is there, I will find it." Then he kissed his mother, strapped his snowshoes on, took a stout stick, and started up the mountain-side.

Oh, how cold it was! The wind whistled through the bare tree-tops and the snow blew in his face, but on he tramped, pushing and poking about with his stick to find the brown herb.

"I must find it," he said, as it grew colder and colder, "I must find it, for that alone will cure my dear mother."

Up and up he climbed. The snow grew harder and harder under his feet. His fingers ached and he grew numb with cold, but he would not turn back.

II

At last he paused to rest against a sheltering rock. There, from a cleft in the rock, grew a most wonderful flower. It was pure and white, and sparkled like a diamond in the sunlight. He could look deep down into its very heart, and its perfume was like the breath of a million roses.

As Arnold stooped to pick the flower, a voice within him seemed to say, "Wait, Arnold, wait until you find the brown herb for your mother."

So Arnold left the wonderful flower and trudged on, poking about in the snow. As he approached the mountain top and as the sun was about to set, he found the brown herb, put it safely in his pocket, and started toward the sheltering rock.

"Now I may pick the flower," he said to himself. But when he reached the rock, it was gone. In its place stood a little brown dwarf, bowing and taking off his hat to Arnold.

9

"Oh, please tell me where I may find the wonderful flower!" cried

Arnold. "It grew right here, where we are now standing."

"Ah," said the dwarf, "you have

seen the magic flower! Only the pure in heart can look on it, and no one can pick this flower, but the memory of it is yours as long as your heart is clean."

"But come with me," continued the dwarf, "a boy who leaves the magic flower that he may serve his mother, shall be rewarded."

Then the strangest thing happend. The side of the mountain opened like a door, the little dwarf stepped along in front to show the way and Arnold found himself in a beautiful castle. It was so bright that it dazzled his eyes. From room to room they went, and in every room were piles and piles of precious stones—emeralds, diamonds, rubies, and pearls.

"Help yourself, Arnold," said the

11

dwarf, as he brought out a strong bag for Arnold to fill. "Take home as many as you can carry."

III

So Arnold filled his bag with the precious stones, taking a number of the sparkling diamonds because they reminded him of the magic flower. "I can look into the heart of the diamond as I looked into the heart of the pure, white flower," he said.

At last the bag was full, and Arnold suddenly found himself in the snow on the mountain-side, with the bag on his shoulder. He felt in his pocket, found the brown herb was still there, and started for home as fast as the snowshoes could take him.

"Mother, Mother!" he cried, as
he ran and threw his arms around
her. "See! I have the brown herb."

"And we are not poor any longer,"
he shouted, as he emptied the bag
on the floor.

They made tea of the brown

herb and as soon as the mother tasted it, she was well again.

Then Arnold told her about the wonderful flower and what the dwarf had said about it.

The strong bag of jewels always remained full, and Arnold never lost the memory of the pure, white flower.

14

THE TIGER, THE BRAHMAN, AND THE JACKAL

I

Long, long ago when strange things happened, a tiger was caught in a trap. He tried in vain to break the bars, and rolled and frothed with rage because he failed.

Just by chance a poor Brahman came that way.

"Let me out of this cage, O pious man!" cried the tiger.

"Nay, nay, friend," replied the Brahman, "you would eat me if I did."

"No, no, I would not," swore the tiger. "Indeed, I should be so grateful that I would be your slave."

The tiger sighed and sobbed and swore till the pious Brahman's heart softened and at last he opened the cage door.

Out jumped the tiger and at once seized the poor man and cried, "What a fool you are! Don't you know that I am frightfully hungry and I shall surely eat you?"

The Brahman pleaded so feelingly for his life that the tiger at last said that he would leave the decision to the first three things the Brahman should choose.

So the Brahman asked a fig tree to decide the matter, but the tree replied coldly, "You need not complain—I must shade and shelter all who pass by and what do they do but tear down my branches and trample them. Don't weep and complain, be a man!"

Then the sad Brahman put his case before a buffalo whom he saw turning

16

a well wheel in the field. But his
reply pleased the Brahman no better.

Then the Brahman in great fear
asked the road.

"My good sir," said the road, "you are foolish to expect better treatment. See my state—I am useful to all but am thanked by none."

II

Then the Brahman turned sadly back and prepared to die. But on the way he met a jackal who called out, "Why, what's the matter, my good man? You look as if you had lost your last friend."

The Brahman told him all that had happened.

"How very confusing!" said the jackal. "Would you mind telling it over again? I don't seem to understand how all this happened."

The Brahman told it all over again but the jackal seemed as confused as ever. "It's very strange," said he, shaking his head, "but it

18

all seems to go in one ear and out of the other. Let us go to the place where it happened and then perhaps I will understand."

So they went to the cage where

the tiger was waiting and found him sharpening his teeth.

"You've been gone a long time," growled the beast savagely, "but now I'll begin my dinner."

"Give me just five minutes," pleaded the wretched Brahman, "that I may explain matters to the jackal who is slow in understanding."

III

The tiger at last consented and the Brahman told the story over again, not missing a single point and making the tale as long as possible.

"Oh, my poor head! oh, my poor head!" cried the jackal. "Let me see! How did it all begin? You were in the cage, and the tiger came walking by."

"Nonsense," cried the tiger, "how very foolish you are! I was in the cage."

"Of course," cried the jackal, pretending to tremble, "yes, I was in the cage—no, I wasn't—dear! dear! where are my brains? Let me see—the tiger was in the Brahman, and the cage came walking by—no, that's not it either! Don't mind me, but begin your dinner, for I shall never understand!"

"Yes, you shall!" replied the tiger, in a rage, "I'll make you understand! I am the tiger!"

"Yes, kind sir!"

"And this is the Brahman!"

"Yes, kind sir!"

"And this is the cage!"

"Yes, kind sir!"

"And I was in the cage. Do you understand?"

"Yes—no—please, kind sir!"

21

"Please what?" cried the tiger angrily.

"Please, kind sir, how did you get in?"

"Why in the usual way, of course!"

"But oh, dear me! My head is beginning to spin again! Please do not be angry, kind sir, but what is the usual way?"

At this the tiger lost all patience, and jumping into the cage, cried, "This is the way! Now do you see how it was?"

"Certainly!" smiled the jackal as he quickly shut the door, "and if you will allow me to say so I think you will remain where you are!"

MAKING THE BEST OF IT

I

"What a dreary day this is!" said the old gray goose to the brown hen, as they stood at the hen-house window and watched the falling snow which covered every nook and corner of the farmyard.

"Yes, indeed," said the brown hen, "I would be almost willing to be made into chicken pie on such a day."

She had scarcely stopped talking, when the Pekin duck said, fretfully, "I am dreadfully hungry," and a little flock of speckled chickens all huddled together wailed in sad chorus, "And we're so thirsty!"

In fact, the feathered folk in the

hen-house were very cross and discontented. Since the farmer's boy fed them early in the morning, they had been given nothing to eat or drink, and as hour after hour went by, and the cold winter wind howled around their house, it was no wonder they felt deserted.

The handsome white rooster, however, appeared quite as happy as usual, and that is saying a great deal, for a jollier old fellow than he was never seen in a farmyard. Sunshine, rain, or snow were all the same to him, and he crowed quite as loudly in stormy as in fair weather.

"Well," he said, laughing heartily, as his bright eyes glanced about the hen-house, "you all seem to be having a fit of the dumps."

Nobody answered the white roos-

24

ter, but a faint cluck or two came from some hens who immediately put their heads under their wings, as if ashamed of having spoken at all.

This was too much for the white rooster. He stood first on one yellow foot and then on the other, turned his head from side to side and said, "Well, we are a lively set! Anyone would think, to look in here, that we were surrounded by a band of hungry foxes."

Just then a daring little white bantam rooster hopped down from his perch, and strutting over to the big rooster, created quite a stir among the feathered folk by saying, "We are all lively enough when our crops are full, but when we're starving the wonder is that we can hold our heads up at all. If I ever

25

see that farmer's boy again, I'll—
I'll peck his foot."

"You won't see him until he
feeds us," said the white rooster,
"and then I guess you will peck
the corn."

"Oh, oh!" moaned the brown hen,
"don't mention a peck of corn."

II

"Madam," remarked the white
rooster, bowing politely, "your
trouble is my own—that is, I'm
hungry, too. But we might be
worse off; we might be on our
way to market in a box. Then,
too, suppose we haven't enough to
eat to-day, at least we have room
enough to stretch our wings."

"Why, that is a fact," answered
the brown hen, and all the feathered family stretched their wings,

preened their feathers and looked a trifle happier.

"Now," continued the rooster, "suppose we have a little music to cheer us up and help pass the hours until roosting time. We will all crow—there, I beg your pardon, ladies, I am sorry you can't crow —we will sing a merry song. Will you be kind enough to start a lively tune, Mrs. Brown Hen?"

The brown hen shook herself proudly, tossed her head back and began, "Cut-cut-cut-ca-dah-cut, cut-cut-cut-ca-dah-cut," and in less than two minutes everyone in the hen-house had joined her.

Now the horses, cows, and sheep were not far away, and hearing the happy voices in the hen-house, they, too, joined in the grand chorus, while

the pigs did their best to squeal
louder than all the rest. Higher
and higher, stronger and stronger,
rose the chorus; louder and louder
quacked the ducks, and shriller and
shriller squeaked the pigs.

They were all so happy that
they forgot their hunger until the
door of the hen-house burst open,
and in came three chubby children,
each carrying a dish full of steam-
ing chicken food.

"Don't stop your music, Mr. Rooster," said the little girl, who was so snugly bound up that you could scarcely see her dear little face. "You see, we were so lonesome that we didn't know what to do, but when we heard all you folks singing out here in your house, we laughed and laughed until we nearly cried. Then we went to tell Jack about you. He was lonesome, too—poor Jack's sick with a sore throat—and he said, 'Why those poor hens; they haven't been fed since morning!'"

"Cock-a-doodle-doo!" said the white rooster. "This comes of making the best of things. Cock-a-doodle-doo!" and nobody asked him to stop crowing.

29

YOUR FLAG AND MY FLAG

Your flag and my flag!
And how it flies today
In your land and my land
And half a world away!
Rose-red and blood-red,
The stripes forever gleam,
Snow-white and soul-white—
The good forefather's dream.
Sky-blue and true-blue, and stars
    to gleam aright,
The gloried guidon of the day,
    a shelter through the night!

Your flag and my flag!
To every star and stripe,
The drums beat as hearts beat
And fifers shrilly pipe!
Your flag and my flag!

A blessing in the sky;
Your hope and my hope,
It never hides a lie!
Home land and far land and half
the world around,
Old Glory hears our glad salute, and
ripples to the sound.

Your flag and my flag!
And oh! How much it holds!
Your land and my land
Secure within its folds!
Your heart and my heart
Beat quicker at the sight,
Sun-kissed and wind-tossed,
The Red and Blue and White!
The one flag—the great flag—the
flag for me and you—
Glorified all else beside, the Red
and White and Blue!

WILBUR D. NESBIT.

31

THE ROBINS' NEST

In the top of a tall house there lived three little children. A beautiful elm tree grew close to the window of the room in which they played.

They loved this big tree. In the spring they watched for the coming of its green leaves, and in the summer they looked for birds hidden from the sun in its cool branches.

One spring something wonderful happened. Two robins built a nest in the old elm tree. The children were greatly excited. They hung out pieces of twine for them to use and little Rosa, standing on tiptoe, peeped over the window sill and called softly, "There they are! There they are!"

32

From their window the children could look down into the nest and see pretty blue eggs and later, wide-open bills begging for food. The most exciting time was when four little robins stood on the edge of the nest and spread their wings. Three of them fluttered safely to the tree; but the fourth, catching its claw in the edge of the nest, went tumbling into the muddy street.

Mary ran swiftly down stairs, and lifted the trembling little thing into her apron. Then she put the poor bird on some soft cotton in a box. When her father came, he found that its wing was hurt, so he fastened the box outside the window where the mother bird could find her little one.

For several weeks the mother

bird came and fed it; but it soon grew tame, and as it could never fly, the children's father made a cage for it. The children were very happy in nursing the little robin until it was strong and well. Then there were four playmates in the top of the tall house, and the gayest of them all was the little bird that sat in the window and filled the room with its singing.

THE BROWNIES

I

Such wonderful stories as grand-mother told Johnnie and Tommy! Stories of ghosts and hobgoblins, of dwarfs and fairies; and once she told them about a brownie that was said to have lived in their own family, long ago, a brownie who did all manner of wonderful and useful things.

"He was a little fellow no larger than Tommy," she said, "but very active and very shy. He slept by the kitchen fire, and no one ever saw him, but early in the morning, when all the family were in their beds, this brownie would get up, sweep the room, build the fire, spread the table, milk the cow, churn the cream, bring the water, scrub and dust, until there was not a speck of dirt anywhere to be seen."

The children liked this story very much, and how they did wish such a brownie would come to live in their house now! Over and over again they said, "Was there really and truly a brownie, grandmother, and did he really help all the people as you say? How we wish he would come back again! Why he could mind the baby and tidy the room and bring in the wood and wait on you, grandmother! Can't we do something to get him back again?"

"I don't know, my dears," said the grandmother, "but they used to say in my young days, that if one set a bowl of bread and milk, or even a pan of clear water for him over night, he would be sure to come and would do all the work just for that."

"Oh, let us try it!" said both boys, and one ran to get a pan, and the other to fetch fresh water from the well, for they knew, poor hungry lads, that there was no bread or milk in the house. Their father was a poor tailor, and he could scarcely earn enough money to buy **food** for them all.

His wife had died when the baby was born and he could not make as many coats as before, for he must now do all the work of the house. Johnnie and Tommy were idle and lazy and too thoughtless to help their father, although they were fine lads of five and seven.

II

One night Tommy had a wonderful dream. He thought he went down in the meadow by the old mill pond, and there he saw an owl who shook her feathers, rolled her great eyes, and called, "Tuwhit, Tuwhoo!

Tuwhoo, whoo-o-o-o! Tommy, what are you doing way down here this time of night?"

"Please, I came to find the brownies," said Tommy. "Can you tell me where they live, ma'am?"

"Tuwhoo, tuwhoo!" screamed the old owl. "So it's the brownies you are after, is it? Tuwhoo, tuwhoo! Go look in the mill pond. Tuwhoo, tuwhoo! Go look in the water at midnight, and you'll see one. By the light of the moon a brownie you'll see, to be sure, but such a lazy one! Tuwhoo, tuwhoo!" screamed the old owl, and flapping her wings, she went sailing away in the moonlight.

"The mill pond, at midnight, by moonlight!" thought Tommy. "What could the old owl mean?" It was midnight then, and moonlight, too, and there he was right down by the water. "Silly old thing," said Tommy, "brownies don't live in the water."

But for all that Tommy went to the bank and peeped in. The moon was shining as bright as day, and what do you suppose he saw? Why just a picture of himself in the water and that was all. "Humph! I'm no brownie," said he to himself, but the longer he looked the harder he thought.

At last he said, "Am I a brownie? Perhaps I am one after all. Grandmother said they are about as large as I, and the old owl said that I would see a very lazy one if I looked in the water. Am I lazy? That must be what she meant. I am the brownie myself."

41

The longer he thought about it the surer he was that he must be a brownie. "Why," he said, "if I am one, Johnnie must be another, then there are two of us. I'll go home and tell Johnnie all about it."

Off he ran as fast as his legs could carry him, and just as he was calling, "Johnnie, Johnnie! We are brownies! The old owl told me!" he found himself wide awake, sitting up in bed, rubbing his eyes, while Johnnie lay fast asleep by his side. The first faint rays of morning light were just creeping in at their chamber window. "Johnnie, Johnnie, wake up! I have something to tell you!"

After telling his brother all about his strange dream, Tommy said, "Let us play we really are brownies, John, even if we are not. It will be such fun for once to surprise father and grandmother. We will keep out of sight and tell about it afterwards. Oh, do come! It will be such fun!"

So these two brownies put on their clothes in a great hurry and crept softly down to the kitchen, where at first there seemed enough work for a dozen brownies to do. Tommy built up a blazing fire, and while the kettle was boiling, he swept the untidy floor. Johnnie dusted, placed his grandmother's chair, got the cradle ready for the baby, and spread the table.

Just as everything was in order they heard their father's footstep on the stairs. "Run!" whispered Tommy, "or he will see us." So the boys scampered away to their bed in the loft and pretended to be fast asleep when their father called them to breakfast.

The poor tailor was fairly beside himself with delight and believed that the brownie he had heard so much about in his childhood had really come back again. The old grandmother was delighted, too, and said, "What did I tell you, son Thomas? I always knew there were real brownies."

Although being brownies was fun for the boys, it was hard work, too, and they sometimes thought they would leave off, but then they would

44

think of their hard-working father
and would grow quite ashamed.

Things were so much better at
home now than they used to be.
The tailor never scolded, the grand-

mother was more cheerful, the baby
was less fretful, and the house was
always tidy. The tailor had more
time for his work, now that the
brownies helped, so he could make
more coats and more money. The
boys did not go hungry to bed as
they used to, for there was always
bread and milk enough, and a great
bowlful to spare that they set each
night for the brownie.

IV

At last the tailor said, "I am going
to do something for that brownie.
He has done so much for us all."
So he cut and stitched the neatest
little coat you ever saw, for he said,
"I have always heard that a
brownie's clothes are ragged, and
our brownie will need this, I know."

When the coat was done it just fitted Tommy and was very fine to see, all stitched with gold thread and covered with brave brass buttons.

That night the little coat was placed by the bowl of milk set for the brownie. When the early morning came, the tailor was awakened by the sound of laughter in the kitchen. "It's the brownie," thought he, and getting out of bed he crept softly down the stairs.

But when he reached the kitchen, instead of the brownie, he saw Tommy and Johnnie sweeping and making the fire, and dusting and setting the table. Tommy had put on the coat that the tailor had made for the brownie. He was skipping about in it laughing and calling to Johnnie to see how fine he looked, but saying, "I wish he had made it to fit you, John."

"Boys, what does all this mean?" cried the tailor. "Tommy, why have you put on that coat?"

When the boys saw their father they ran to him and tried to tell him all about it. "There is no brownie, father," they cried, "but we have done the work. And dear father, we are sorry that we were lazy and idle so long, but we mean to be real brownies now, and help you till we grow to be big men." The poor tailor was so happy that he knew not what to say, and there were tears in his eyes as he kissed each little son.

Tommy and Johnnie kept their promise and continued being brownies until they went away to homes

48

Caroline.   And Caroline hugged and
kissed and cried over Timothy Titus
and gave him to Mr. Davis, who put

him in a basket and tied a bag
over it.

"I guess he'll be all right," said Mr. Davis. "Good day," and away rumbled the apple cart.

II

But as soon as the apple cart was out of sight, Caroline began to mourn. She stood at the window with a very doleful face, looking across the river at Mr. Davis's big white house. The sky had all at once grown cloudy, and the wind began to blow. And, as if to make a bad matter worse, Toots woke up and flew around the room in a fit.

"It is all because he knows that Timothy Titus is gone," sobbed Caroline, running to hide her head in her mother's lap. "How would I feel if Teddy were given away, where I'd never see him any more? And the apples are bitterish, too, and I don't like them. O, dear!"

But mother said that perhaps Timothy Titus would come home again. "I've heard of such things," she said. And then she told Caroline a story about a cat who traveled forty miles back to her old home.

"But I don't believe Timothy Titus can," sighed Caroline, brightening up a little, "because he's over the river, and there isn't any bridge —only the ferry-boat. I 'most know he can't."

"Oh, stranger things than that have happened," said mother, hopefully.

But she was as surprised as Caroline was the next morning. When the kitchen door was opened —what do you think? In walked

Timothy Titus, as large as life but a little bit draggled as to his fur and muddy around his paws!

"Hello!" said father.

"Well, well!" said mother. "Why Timothy Titus!"

Just at that minute Caroline came running out in her nightgown. She gave one look, and then she snatched Timothy Titus up in her arms.

"Oh, oh!" she screamed, too full of joy to do anything else for a minute. "Oh, you darling cat! How did he get here, mother?"

"I'm sure I can't tell," said mother.

Neither could anyone else unless it was the ferry-man. When father questioned him, he said he did think he remembered seeing a little black and white cat sitting under the seat the night before. But he

over his ears, and then Li'l' Hannibal ran away!

He went down the big road past all the cabins. He went under the fence and across the cotton fields.

He went through the pine grove past the schoolhouse, stooping down low—so the schoolmistress couldn't see him—and then he went way, way off into the country.

When he was a long way from town, Li'l' Hannibal met a possum loping along by the edge of the road, and the possum stopped and looked at Li'l' Hannibal.

"How do? Where you going, Li'l' Hannibal?" asked the possum.

Li'l' Hannibal sat down by the side of the road and took off his straw hat to fan himself, for he felt quite warm, and he said,

"I've run away, Br'er Possum, my gran'mammy and my gran'daddy kept me toting, toting for them all the time. I don't like to work, Br'er Possum."

"Poor Li'l' Hannibal!" said the possum, sitting up and scratching himself. "Any special place you bound for?"

"I don't think so," said Li'l' Hannibal, for he was getting tired, and he had come away without any breakfast.

"You come along with me, Li'l'

Hannibal," said the possum; "I can take you somewhere."

III

So the possum and Li'l' Hannibal went along together, the possum loping along by the side of the road and Li'l' Hannibal going very slowly in the middle of the road, for his shoes were full of sand and it hurt his toes. They went on and on until they came all at once, to a sort of open space in the woods and then they stopped. There was a big company there—Br'er Rabbit and Br'er Partridge, and Br'er Jay Bird and Br'er Robin, and Old Miss Guinea Hen.

"Poor Li'l' Hannibal has come to see you," said the possum. "Li'l' Hannibal has run away from his gran'mammy and gran'daddy."

Li'l' Hannibal hung his head as if he was ashamed, but nobody noticed him. They were all as busy as they could be, and so he just sat down on a pine stump and watched them.

Each one had his own special work and he was keeping right at it. Br'er Robin was gathering all the holly berries from the south side of the holly tree and singing as he worked,

"Cheer up, cheer-u-p!"

Br'er Partridge was building a new house down low in the bushes. As he hurried back and forth with twigs, he would stop and drum a little, he felt so happy to be busy.

Br'er Jay Bird was taking corn down below. You know that is what Br'er Jay Bird does all the time. He takes one kernel of corn in his bill to the people down below and then comes back for another. It is a very long trip to take with one kernel of corn, but Br'er Jay

Bird doesn't seem to mind how hard he works.

Old Miss Guinea Hen was almost the busiest of the whole company, for she was laying eggs. As soon as ever she laid one, she would get up on a low branch and screech, "Catch it! Catch it! Catch it!" loud enough to deafen everybody.

IV

But Li'l' Hannibal was most interested to see what Br'er Rabbit was doing. Br'er Rabbit had on a little apron, and he kept bringing things in his market basket. Then he cooked the things over a fire back in the bushes, and when it got to be late in the afternoon, he spread a tablecloth on a big stump and then he pounded on his stewpan

"Why Li'l' Hannibal, where've you been all day?" asked his gran'-daddy.

"Oh, Li'l' Han," said his gran'-mammy, "here's your corn mush. I kept it warm on the hearth, but before you eat your supper, Li'l' Han, just take your li'l' basket and run round to the chicken house for a couple of eggs."

So Li'l' Hannibal took his li'l' basket, and he started for those eggs, singing all the way. You see, he was mighty glad to be at home, and toting again.

See Teachers Manual, Page 44

THE MOUSE, THE BIRD
AND THE BEE

A mouse, a bird and a bee one day met under a large elm tree. The mouse, feeling very friendly toward the others, suggested that they all keep house together.

"Yes," said the bird, "we will build the nest in the branch of this tree just above our heads. We shall be far away from our enemies, the cats, there. The wind will rock our babies to sleep."

"But my babies squeak if they

are rocked," said Mrs. Mouse. "They do not like it. Besides they would be sure to fall if they were up so high. They would break their little necks. Then, too, it is so light it would make their eyes weak. No, the best place for our nest is in the ground, inside a hollow tree. It is warm and dark there, and no one will find us."

"In the ground, indeed!" said the bird. "So you think I would take my babies into the ground? They would smother there. Besides, they need all the light they can get."

"You had better not quarrel, but listen to me," said the bee. "The best place to build is in this beehive. It is not so high but that we can carry honey in without much trouble. If we lived in the elm branch I should be too tired to carry the honey so high. If we lived in the ground I should catch cold. So let us build in this nice hive."

"And have the cat eat our babies? No, indeed!" said the mouse, and "No, indeed!" echoed the bird.

"Well, since we cannot agree, let each build his own home. The bird can build on the branch of the elm tree. I will build in this hive under the elm tree. So we shall see each other often, even though we do not live together."

"Squeak, squeak!" said the mouse as she ran to the hollow tree.

"Buzz, buzz!" said the bee as he began to gather honey.

"Tir-a-lee, tir-a-lee," sang the bird, high on the bough of the old elm tree.

answered Blunder, discontentedly. But still he went on up the brook, till hot and tired, and out of patience at seeing neither crow nor pine, he sat down under a great tree to rest. There he heard tiny voices squabbling.

"Get out! Go away, I tell you! It has been knock! knock! knock! at my door all day, till I am tired out. First a wasp, and then a bee, and then another wasp, and then another bee, and now you. Go away! I won't let another one in today."

"But I want my honey."

"And I want my nap."

"I will come in."

"You shall not."

"You are a miserly old elf."

"And you are a brute of a bee."

And looking about him, Blunder spied a bee, quarreling with a morning-glory elf, who was shutting up the morning-glory in his face.

"Elf, do you know which is the way to the Wishing-Gate?"

"No," said the elf, "I don't know anything about geography. I was always too delicate to study. But if you will keep on this path, you will meet the Dream-man, coming down from fairyland, with his bags of dreams on his shoulder, and if anybody can tell you about the Wishing-Gate, he can."

"But how can I find him?" asked Blunder, more and more impatient.

"I don't know, I am sure," answered the elf, "unless you should look for him."

So there was no help for it but to go on, and presently Blunder passed the Dream-man, asleep under a witch-hazel, with his bags of good and bad dreams laid over him to keep him from fluttering away.

IV

But Blunder had a habit of not using his eyes; for at home, when told to find anything, he always said, "I don't know where it is," or "I can't find it," and then his mother or sister went straight and found it for him. So he passed the Dream-man without seeing him, and went on till he stumbled on Jack-o'-Lantern.

"Can you show me the way to the Wishing-Gate?" said Blunder.

"Certainly, with pleasure," answered Jack, and catching up his lantern, set out at once.

Blunder followed close, but in watching the lantern, he forgot to look at his feet, and fell into a hole filled with black mud.

"I say! the Wishing-Gate is not

down there," called out Jack, whisking off among the tree tops.

"But I can't come up there," whimpered Blunder.

"That is not my fault, then," answered Jack, merrily dancing out of sight.

"Only my pans, master," answered the cook. And as he could see nothing amiss, the old goblin went grumbling upstairs again, while the cook put the shoes on Blunder. They took him up the chimney, and landed him in a meadow, safe enough, but so miserable! He was cross, he was disappointed, he was hungry.

It was dark, he did not know the way home, and seeing an old stile, he climbed up, and sat down on the top of it for he was too tired to stir. Just then along came the South Wind, with his pockets crammed full of showers, and, as he happened to be going Blunder's way, he took Blunder home.

Of course the boy was glad enough, only he would have liked it better if the Wind had not laughed all the way. For what would you think, if you were walking along a road with a fat old gentleman who went chuckling to himself, and slapping his knees, and poking himself, till he was purple in the face, and then would burst out in a great windy roar of laughter every other minute?

"What are you laughing at?" asked Blunder, at last.

"At two things I saw in my travels," answered the Wind, "a hen that died of starvation, sitting on an empty peck measure that stood in front of a bushel of grain, and a little boy who sat on the top of the Wishing-Gate, and came home because he could not find it."

"What, what's that?" cried Blunder. But just then he found himself at home. There sat his fairy godmother by the fire, her mouse skin cloak hung up on a peg, and toeing off a spider's silk stocking an eighth of an inch long, and though everybody else cried, "What luck?" and "Where is the Wishing-Gate?" she said nothing.

"I don't know where it is," answered Blunder. "I couldn't find it," and then he told the story of his troubles.

"Poor boy!" said his mother kissing him, while his sister ran to bring him some bread and milk.

"Yes, that is all very fine," cried his godmother, pulling out her needles, and rolling up her ball of silk, "but now hear my story."

"There was once a little boy who must needs go to the Wishing-Gate, and his fairy godmother showed him the road as far as the turn, and told him to ask the first owl he met what to do then."

"But this little boy seldom uses his eyes, so he passed the first owl and waked up the wrong owl, so he passed the water sprite, and found only a frog; so he sat down under the pine tree, and never saw the crow; so he passed the Dream-man, and ran after the Jack-o'-Lantern; so he tumbled down the goblin's chimney, and couldn't find the shoes and the closet and the chest and the cloak; and so he sat on the top of the Wishing-Gate till the

pine trees whispering in the wind
and the lapping of the water on the
shore. When he saw the firefly
flitting through the dusk of evening,
lighting the bushes with the twinkle
of its candle, he sang the song
Nokomis taught him:

"Wah-wah-taysee, little firefly,
Little, flitting, white fire insect;
Little, dancing, white fire
    creature,
Light me with your little candle
Ere upon my bed I lay me,
Ere in sleep I close my eyelids."

All the strange sights and sounds
of nature filled Hiawatha with
wonder. Then he would come to
Nokomis and ask her questions. He
saw the rainbow in the heaven
arching the eastern sky and he

whispered to Nokomis, "What is that?"

> And the good Nokomis answered:
> "'Tis the heaven of flowers you see there,
> All the wild flowers of the forest,
> All the lilies of the prairie,
> When on earth they fade and perish,
> Blossom in the heaven above us."

One dark night the hooting of the owls disturbed him and he was afraid but good Nokomis said,

> "That is but the owl and owlet,
> Talking in their native language,
> Talking, scolding at each other!"

the thicket. His heart trembled like the leaves about him as the deer came down the pathway.

Hiawatha rose on one knee and aimed an arrow. The roebuck started and listened with one foot uplifted. He stamped with all his hoofs together and leaped to meet the arrow as it stung him.

Very proudly Hiawatha bore the deer homeward to old Nokomis and Iagoo. Nokomis made a cloak from the deer's skin for Hiawatha and held a great banquet in his honor. All the Indians from the village came to the feast. They praised the little hunter and called him Strong-Heart, Soan-ge-taha.

HIAWATHA AND MUDJEKEEWIS

I

As the years passed by Hiawatha grew to manhood and became very strong, wise and skilful. He was the bravest hunter in all the land. He did everything better than anyone else in the tribe. Still his heart was very true and his thoughts were of his people and how he could make them good and happy.

Often he wondered about his father, Mudjekeewis, and then he would question Nokomis. She told him of his father's great strength in the kingdom of the West Wind, in the land of the Golden Sunset.

Hiawatha wanted to visit his father, but Nokomis feared that some harm might befall him. But at last he decided to take the journey.

Dressed for travel, armed for hunting, with eagle feathers on his head and belt of wampum round his waist, Hiawatha started for the land of the Golden Sunset.

After many weary days of travel, he reached the summit of the Great Mountain and found Mudjekeewis seated upon the throne. Great joy

into the valley. With this old arrow-maker lived his beautiful daughter, whom he had named Minnehaha, Laughing Water.

Hiawatha saw the beautiful maiden and thought of her often during his homeward journey. He longed to see her again, but he knew he must first help his people.

HIAWATHA THE LEADER

I

After Hiawatha's return from the Land of the West Wind, he became the hero and leader of his tribe. Not only was he brave, strong and wise, but he was kind and good. He wanted to make the life of his people easier and happier.

He built a wigwam in a lonely spot near the lake. Here, he went alone to fast and pray to Gitche Manito, the Great Spirit. He prayed that he might bring some good to his people. During the first days of his fasting he saw all the wild creatures as he walked through the leafy woods. As he neared the brink of the river he saw many wild fruits trailing over the branches. As he sat by the lake, he heard the birds' music above him and saw the fishes in the water.

Then he cried aloud, "Master of Life! Must our lives depend on these wild things? Is there nothing we can do to have food at all times?"

II

On the fourth day of his fasting, he saw a youth approaching in the purple twilight. He was dressed in green and yellow garments. When

invited all the tribe. For many
years they lived in peace and plenty
with the people of all nations.

THE FAMINE

I

There came a long, dreary winter, when ice covered the lake and snow spread a white mantle over the

landscape. The people were unable to get fish from the streams or animals from the forests. All the corn that had been stored from the

harvests had been used. There was nothing left. Everyone was cold and hungry. Many Indians died from famine and fever. Sickness visited the wigwam of Hiawatha and beautiful Minnehaha became very ill.

Great sorrow filled the heart of Hiawatha as, wrapped in furs and armed for hunting, he rushed forth into the empty forest in search of food. He cried aloud to Gitche Manito, the Mighty,

"Give your children food, O Father!
Give us food or we must perish,
Give me food for Minnehaha!"

But in answer there came only the echo of his cry.

At home old Nokomis was waiting anxiously for Hiawatha to return with food, for she knew that Minne-

121

haha was very ill.   At last Minnehaha beckoned to her and said,

"Hark! I hear the Falls of Min-
    nehaha
Calling to me from a distance."

Far away in the forest, Hiawatha seemed to hear the voice of Minnehaha calling him back. Emptyhanded, heavy-hearted, he hurried homeward. In the stillness of the night he reached the wigwam, but it was too late. As he fell at the feet of Laughing Water, he knew that never again would she run to meet him or follow him lightly through the forest.

For seven long days Hiawatha sat in silence with his great sorrow. Then he buried Minnehaha underneath the waving hemlocks. In his loneliness he cried,

"Farewell, O my Laughing Water,
All my heart is buried with you,
All my thoughts go onward with
you,

To the Islands of the Blessed,
To the land of the Hereafter."

When the terrible winter was over
and the warm spring days came
back, Hiawatha worked again among
his people. Though sad and lonely
he was so kind and thoughtful that
his tribe called him, "Hiawatha the
Beloved."

HIAWATHA'S DEPARTURE

I

One day, Iagoo, the great story
teller, returned from a long journey
through a strange country. All the
Indians came to hear him tell of his
wonderful adventures. He told them
he had seen a body of water much
larger than the lake of Gitche
Gumee. Then he described a great
white winged canoe that came sailing

over this big sea of water, and told of
the many white people that filled **it.**

The Indians thought he was boast-
ing and would not believe it. But

when Hiawatha came forward to explain they listened to every word. He said, "What Iagoo says is true, for I have seen a vision and know that the Great Spirit is sending the white men to you with a message. Treat them kindly. They have come to be your friends."

> "Listen to their words of wisdom,
>   Listen to the truth they tell you,
>   For the Master of Life has sent
>   them
>   From the land of light and
>   morning."

II

Then Hiawatha told them that his work among them was finished and that he was going to leave them and go away for a long and distant journey.

He bade them farewell and turned toward the shore of the shining lake where his birch canoe was waiting in the golden glow of the setting sun. As he launched forth into the water, he whispered softly "Westward! Westward! To the Home of Laughing Water!"

"Thus departed Hiawatha,
　Hiawatha the beloved,
　In the glory of the sunset
　In the purple mists of evening
　To the Islands of the Blessed,
　To the land of the Hereafter."

THE LARK AND THE FARMER

A lark once had her nest in a wheat field. Every day she flew off to find food for her young ones.

One day when she was away the farmer came into the field. "This wheat is ripe," he said. "I will get my neighbors to help me cut it."

When the lark came home her young ones told her what they had heard. They were so badly frightened that they begged the mother bird to move out of the field at once.

"There is no hurry," she said. "If he waits for his neighbors, he will have to wait a long time."

The next day the farmer came again.

But I shall name you the fisher-
men three:
Wynken,
Blynken,
And Nod.

Wynken and Blynken are two little
eyes,
And Nod is a little head:
And the wooden shoe that sailed
the skies
Is a wee one's trundle-bed.

So shut your eyes while mother
   sings
   Of wonderful sights that be,
And you shall see the beautiful
   things
   As you rock in the misty sea,
   Where the old shoe rocked the
   fishermen three:
      Wynken,
      Blynken,
      And Nod.

EUGENE FIELD.

THE TRUTHFUL MIRROR

I

Once upon a time there lived a king who had a very beautiful wife. This queen was proud of her beauty and envious of all her fair maidens. Over and over she said to each of them, "Who is the fairest of us all?" And the maidens, fearing to offend her, answered, "Thou art fairest of us all."

On his return from a distant journey, the king brought the queen a wonderful mirror to hang on her wall. Now this proved to be a magic mirror, and when anyone stood before it and asked a question it always answered truthfully.

The queen loved this mirror more

than any of her jewels because it reflected her beauty. One day as she stood before it, she asked the question that was often on her lips,

"Little mirror on the wall,
Who is fairest of us all?"

To her great surprise the mirror spoke these words,

"Lady Queen is tall and grand,
But one is fairer in this land."

136

was very small, and I cannot tell you how pretty and clean it was.

There was a little table covered

Mabel Betsy Hill

with a white tablecloth. On it were seven little plates, seven knives, seven forks, seven spoons, and seven little cups. Round the walls stood seven little beds, close together, with sheets and pillows as white as snow.

141

Snow-white was so hungry that she ate a little from each plate and drank a few drops from each cup, for she did not like to empty one entirely.

Being very tired, she lay down, but she could not make herself comfortable, for one bed was too long and another was too short. Fortunately, the seventh was just right, so there she stayed and fell asleep.

IV

When darkness had fallen, the masters of the house, the seven dwarfs, came home. They lighted their seven candles and immediately saw that some one had been there.

The first said, "Who has been sitting on my stool?"

The second spoke up, "Who has eaten off my plate?"

The third remarked, "Who has been drinking from my little cup?"

And so it went on. Each dwarf found something wrong. At last they came to the beds, and finding them out of order, they looked at each and discovered little Snow-white fast asleep on the seventh bed.

"Oh, what a lovely child!" they cried. The dwarfs were so pleased that they let her sleep all night in the little bed. The seventh dwarf slept with each of his own companions in turn, an hour at a time, and so spent the night.

When Snow-white wakened and saw the seven dwarfs she was frightened, but they were very kind to her, and so her fears soon vanished.

"How did you find your way
here, and what is your name?"
asked the dwarfs.

"My name is Snow-white," replied
the maiden. "The wicked queen
sent the huntsman to kill me. He
spared my life, and I ran the whole
day long till I found your little
house."

The dwarfs answered, "If you will keep our house in order, make the beds, wash, sew and knit, and cook for us, you may live with us and we will protect you."

"I will gladly do all this," replied Snow-white.

So she lived with them and kept their house in order. Every morning they went out among the mountains, to seek iron and gold, and when they came home in the evening Snow-white had supper ready for them.

As Snow-white was left alone all day long, the good dwarfs warned her to beware of the cruel queen.

"She will try to find you," they said, "so let nobody into the house."

V

Having seen Snow-white's blood
on the handkerchief, the queen had
no doubt that she was now the
fairest woman in the world. She
walked up to the mirror and said,

"Little mirror on the wall
Who is fairest of us all?"

The mirror replied,

"Lady queen so grand and tall
Here, you're fairest of them all,
But o'er the hills with seven
dwarfs old,
Lives a fairer one, a hundred
fold."

The queen trembled, for she knew
that the mirror never told her a
falsehood. She felt that the huntsman had deceived her, and that
Snow-white was still alive. She

146

thought of this late and early, for envy gave her no rest. At last she painted her face and dressed herself like an old peddler so that no one could know her. In this disguise, she went over the seven hills to the home of the seven dwarfs, knocked at the door, and cried, "Good ware, cheap! very cheap!"

Snow-white was a friendly little maiden, so she looked out of the window and called, "Good morning, good woman. What have you to sell?"

"Good ware, cheap wares," answered the queen, "bodice laces of all colors," and she drew out some colored silk ones.

"Surely this is an honest peddler," thought Snow-white. "It can do no harm to let her in." So she un-

fastened the door and bought two
of the pretty laces.

"Maiden," said the old woman,

"let me lace these for you properly."
Snow-white feared no harm, so she
148

allowed her bodice to be fastened with the new laces.

Now the old woman was so quick and laced the bodice so tight that Snow-white's breath was stopped, and she fell down as if dead. "Now I am fairest at last," said the queen to herself as she hurried away.

The seven dwarfs came home soon after this and were frightened to find their poor Snow-white lifeless on the floor. They lifted her up and seeing how tightly the bodice was fastened, cut the laces. Then Snow-white began to breathe faintly and slowly returned to life.

When the dwarfs heard what had happened, they said, "The old peddlar woman was the wicked queen. Open the door to no one when we are away."

VI

The cruel queen walked up to her mirror when she reached home and said,

"Truthful mirror on the wall
Who is fairest of us all?"

The mirror answered as before:

"Lady queen, so grand and tall,
Here, you're fairest of them all;
But o'er the hills, with seven
dwarfs old,
Lives a fairer one a hundred
fold."

When she heard this she was so alarmed that all the blood rushed to her heart, for she saw plainly that Snow-white was still alive.

"This time," said she, "I will think of some means that shall surely destroy her;" and with the help of witch-craft, in which she was skilful, she made a poisoned comb.

Then she changed her dress and took the shape of another old woman.

Again she crossed the seven hills to the home of the seven dwarfs, knocked at the door, and cried, "Good wares, very cheap!"

Snow-white looked out and said, "Go away! I dare let no one in."

"You may surely be allowed to look!" answered the old woman, and she drew out the poisoned comb and held it up. The girl was so pleased with it that she let herself be tempted and opened the door.

"Now let me dress your hair properly," said the woman. Poor Snow-white let the old woman begin, but the comb had scarcely touched her hair before the poison worked, and she fell down senseless.

"Now I'm the fairest!" said the wicked woman. "All is over with you now," and went away.

Luckily it was near evening, and the seven dwarfs soon came home. When they found Snow-white lifeless on the ground, they at once suspected the queen. They searched, and found the poisoned comb; and as soon as they had drawn it out, Snow-white came to herself, and told them what had happened. Again they warned her to be careful, and open the door to no one.

VII

Again the queen placed herself before the mirror at home and said,

"Little mirror on the wall,
Who is fairest of us all?"

But again it answered,

"Lady queen so grand and tall
Here, you're fairest of them all.
But o'er the hills with seven
    dwarfs old,
Lives a fairer one, a hundred
    fold."

When she heard the mirror speak thus, she quivered with rage. "Snow-white shall die," she cried, "if it costs my own life."

Then she went to a secret and lonely chamber, where no one ever disturbed her, and fixed an apple with deadly poison. Ripe and rosy cheeked, it was so beautiful to look upon that all who saw it longed for it, but it brought death to any one who should eat it. When the apple was ready she painted her face, disguised herself as a peasant-woman, and journeyed over the seven hills to where the seven dwarfs lived. At the sound of the knock Snow-white put her head out of the window, and said, "I cannot open the door to anybody, for the seven dwarfs have forbidden me to do so."

"Very well," replied the peasant-woman; "I only want to be rid of my apples. Here, I will give you one of them."

"No," said Snow-white, "I dare not take it."

"Are you afraid of being poisoned?" asked the old woman. "Look here, I will cut the apple in two and you shall eat the rosy side, and I, the white."

Now the fruit was so cunningly made that only the rosy side was poisoned. Snow-white longed for the pretty apple, and when she saw the peasant-woman eating it she could resist no longer, but stretched out her hand and took the poisoned half. She had scarcely tasted it when she fell lifeless to the ground.

The queen, laughing loudly,

watched her with a wicked look, and cried, "Oh, fairest one, white as snow, the seven dwarfs cannot awaken you this time."

VIII

And when she asked the mirror at home,

> "Little mirror on the wall,
> Who is fairest of us all?"

The mirror replied,

> "Lady queen, so grand and tall,
> You are fairest of them all."

So her envious heart had as much joy as an envious heart can ever know.

When the dwarfs came home in the evening they found Snow-white lying breathless on the ground. They lifted her up, searched to find whether she had anything poisonous about her, unlaced her, combed her hair, washed her with water and with wine, but all was useless for they could not bring the darling back to life. They laid her on a bier, and all the seven dwarfs stood round it and mourned for her three long days. Then they would have buried her, but she still looked so fresh and lifelike, that they could not do this. They made a coffin of glass, so that she could be seen on all sides, and laid her in it, writing her name outside in letters of gold. Then they placed the coffin on the mountain above, and one of them always stayed by it and guarded it. But there was little need to guard it, for even the wild animals came and mourned for Snow-white; the birds likewise—first an owl, and then a raven, and afterwards a dove.

One day the son of a king chanced to wander into the forest, and came to the dwarfs' house for a night's shelter. He saw the coffin on the mountain with the beautiful Snow-white in it, and read what was written there in letters of gold. Then he said to the dwarfs, "Let me have the coffin! I will give you whatever you like to ask for it."

But the dwarfs answered, "We would not part with it for all the gold in the world."

He said again, "Yet give it to me, for I cannot live without seeing Snow-white, and though she is dead, I will prize and honor her as my beloved."

Then the good dwarfs took pity on him, and gave him the coffin. The prince had it borne away by his servants. They happened to stumble over a bush, and the shock forced the bit of poisoned apple, which Snow-white had tasted, out of her throat. Immediately she opened her eyes, raised the coffin-lid, and sat up alive once more. "Oh," cried she, "where am I?"

The prince answered joyfully, "You are with a prince." Then he told her what had happened and said, "Come with me to my father's castle and be my wife."

Snow-white, well pleased, went with him. Wonderful wedding garments were prepared for her, and all the royal families were invited to the feast. Among these was the wicked queen.

When she found that a new and beautiful queen was to reign so near her own realm, she stood before the mirror and said,

"Truthful mirror on the wall
Who is fairest of us all?"

The mirror answered:

"Lady queen, so grand and tall,
Here, you're the fairest of them all,
But the young queen o'er the mountains old,
Is fairer than you a hundred fold."

Then she resolved not to attend the wedding for she knew her jealousy would know no bounds. But curiosity would not allow her to rest, so at last she determined to go and see who the young queen could be, who was the most beautiful in all the world. When she came, and found that it was Snow-white in all her fair beauty she shook with terror and despair. The evil-hearted woman uttered a curse and could scarcely endure her anguish. She rushed from the palace into the gloomy forest and was never seen again.

I

Far away in the land to which the swallows fly when it is winter lived a king who had eleven sons and one daughter named Elsa. The eleven brothers were princes, and went to school with stars on their breasts and swords by their sides. They wrote with diamond pencils on golden slates, and learned their lessons so quickly and read so easily that every one knew they were princes. Their sister Elsa sat on a little stool of plate-glass, and had a picture book which had cost half a kingdom.

These children were very happy till their mother died. Their father, who was king of the country, had the children cared for by a woman with a beautiful face but a wicked heart. When the king was away, instead of giving the children cakes and apples she gave them sand in a tea-cup and told them to pretend it was cake. Very soon she persuaded the king to send little Elsa into the country to a peasant and his wife. Then she told the king so many untrue things about the young princes, that the king gave her permission to do as she pleased with them.

"Go out into the world and get your own living," said the wicked woman. "Fly like great birds without voices." But she could not make them as ugly as she wished, for they were turned into eleven beautiful wild swans. With a strange sound they flew through the windows of the palace, over the park, to the forest.

It was early in the morning when they passed the peasant's cottage where their sister Elsa was sleeping in her room. They hovered over the roof, twisted their long necks and flapped their wings, but no one heard or saw them. Then they flew high up in the clouds. Over the wide world they soared till they came to a dark wood, which stretched far away to the seashore.

II

Poor little Elsa was alone in her room playing with a green leaf, for she had no other plaything. She made a hole through the leaf and looked through it at the sun. It seemed to her as if she saw her brother's bright eyes. When the warm sun touched her cheeks, she thought of all the kisses they had given her.

One day passed just like another. Sometimes the wind rustled through the leaves of the rosebush and whispered to the roses, "What can be more beautiful than you are?" But the roses shook their heads and said, "Elsa."

When the old woman sat at the cottage door on Sunday and read her hymn-book, the wind fluttered the leaves and said to the book, "What can be more beautiful than the roses?" Then the hymn-book would answer, "Elsa." And the roses and the hymn-book told the truth.

Elsa went home when she was fifteen. When the wicked woman saw the beautiful child she was very angry and her heart was filled with envy. She would have turned Elsa into a swan like her brothers, but she did not dare because the king wanted to see his daughter.

Early one morning the wicked woman went into the bath-room. It was built of marble and had soft cushions trimmed with beautiful tapestry. She took three toads with

her, kissed them and said to one, "When Elsa comes to the bath, sit upon her head that she may become as stupid as you are." Then she said to another, "Sit upon her forehead that she may become ugly like you. Rest upon her heart," she whispered to the third, "that she may become evil hearted."

She put the toads into the clear water and it turned green immediately. Then she called Elsa, undressed her and told her to go into the bath. As Elsa dipped her head under the water, one of the toads sat on her hair, the other on her forehead, and a third over her heart. When she stood up, three red poppies floated on the water. Elsa was too good for witchcraft to have any power over her, and her truth had changed the toads into beautiful flowers.

When the wicked witch saw this, she rubbed Elsa's face with walnut juice to make her skin brown. Then she tangled her beautiful hair till it was impossible to know the beautiful child.

III

When her father saw her, he declared she was not his daughter. No one but the watch-dog and the swallows knew her, and they were only dumb animals. Poor Elsa cried and thought of her eleven brothers, who were all lost. She crept sadly out of the palace and walked all day over fields and meadows, till she came to the great forest. She did not know in what direction to go, but she longed for her brothers and was determined to find them.

Soon night came and she lost her path, but she lay down on the soft moss, said her evening prayer, and leaned her head against the stump of a tree. The lights of hundreds of glow-worms shone in the grass and the moss, like green fire. When she touched a twig, the insects fell down around her, like shooting-stars.

All night long she dreamed of her brothers. She thought they were children again playing together. She saw them writing with their diamond pencils on golden slates, and she was looking at the beautiful picture-book which had cost half a kingdom. They were not writing lines and letters as they used to do, but tales of the noble deeds they had done. Everything in her picture-book was alive. The birds sang, and the people walked out of the book and spoke to Elsa and her brothers.

When she woke, it was day and the sunbeams were shining through the leaves like a golden mist. There was a sweet fragrance from the fresh green grass, and the birds almost perched upon her shoulders. She heard the water rippling from the springs, and all the little streams flowed into a beautiful lake. Thick bushes grew round the lake and there was one place where a deer had trampled the bushes. Through this opening Elsa went down to the water. The lake was so clear that every leaf was reflected in the water, whether it was in the shade or the sunshine.

When Elsa saw her own face, she was frightened, it was so brown and ugly; but when she wet her little hand, and rubbed her forehead her

skin became white again. After
she had washed herself in the fresh
water and braided her long hair, a
more beautiful king's daughter could
not be found in the wide world.
Then she went to the bubbling
spring and drank some water out of
the hollow of her hand. She wan-

Mabel Betsy Hill.

dered farther into the forest and at last found a wild apple tree loaded with fruit. Here she ate her noonday meal, placed props under the boughs, and then went into the gloomy forest.

It was so still that she heard her own footsteps, and the rustling of the withered leaves under her feet. Not a bird was to be seen, not a sunbeam pierced the leafy branches. The night was very dark. Not a single glow-worm glittered in the moss.

IV

Sadly she lay down to sleep, and it seemed to her as if the branches above her parted and the angels looked down on her from heaven. When she woke in the morning she wandered on, but she had not gone far, when she met an old woman with a basket of berries. The woman gave her a few to eat. Elsa asked her if she had seen eleven princes riding through the forest.

"No," said the old woman, "but yesterday I saw eleven swans, with golden crowns on their heads, swimming on the river close by." She led Elsa to a sloping bank, and at the foot of it wound a little river. The trees on its banks stretched their leafy branches across the water towards each other. Here Elsa said good-bye to the kind old woman and walked along by the river till she reached the great open sea.

There before her eyes lay the glorious ocean, with not a sail in sight. But on the foam-covered seaweeds, Elsa found eleven white swan feathers. She gathered them up and held them together in her hand. There were drops of water on them, and she could not tell whether they were dew-drops or tears.

It was lonely on the sea shore, but Elsa did not mind it, for the sea was always changing. If a black cloud arose, the sea looked dark and angry. When the wind blew, the waves turned to white foam. When the wind slept and the clouds glowed with the red sunlight, the sea looked like a rose leaf.

V

Just as the sun was setting, Elsa saw eleven white swans with golden crowns on their heads, flying towards the land, one behind the

other, like a long white ribbon.
Elsa went down to the shore and
hid behind the bushes. The swans
came close to her and flapped their

great white wings. As soon as the sun had disappeared, they shed their feathers and became beautiful princes. They were Elsa's brothers. She cried with joy for she knew them at once. She sprang into their arms and called them by name.

The princes were delighted to see their little sister who had grown so tall and beautiful. They laughed, and they cried and told each other how wickedly the cruel woman had treated them.

"We brothers," said the eldest, "are wild swans as long as the sun is in the sky. When it goes down we are princes again. So we must always be near a resting-place before sunset.

"We do not live here, but in a land that lies across the sea. The way to it is very long, and we pass the night on a rock rising out of the water. There is only room enough for us to stand upon it close together. If the sea is rough, the foam dashes over us, but we thank God for this rock. We stay all night upon it, or we should never see our beloved fatherland, for the journey across the sea takes two of the longest days in the year. We have permission to visit our old home once a year and to stay eleven days. We hover over this forest to catch a glimpse of the palace where our father lives, and where we were born. We can stay only two days longer. Then we must fly away to the beautiful land where we now live, but how can we take you with us? We have neither ship nor boat."

"How can I break this spell?" said their sister.

Elsa thought about it nearly the whole night. She was awakened by the rustling of the swan's wings above her. Her brothers were again changed to birds, and they flew in circles wider and wider, till they

were far away. But the youngest swan stayed behind. He laid his head in his sister's lap and she stroked his wings, as they talked together the whole day.

VI

Towards evening the rest came back, and as the sun went down they became her brothers again. "To-morrow," said one of them, "we shall fly away and we cannot return for a whole year. But we cannot leave you here. Have you courage to go with us?"

"Oh yes, take me with you," said Elsa.

They spent the whole night in weaving a net with willow twigs and rushes. It was very large and strong. Elsa lay down upon it, and when the sun rose, the swans took

up the net with their beaks, and
flew up to the clouds with their
dear sister. The sunbeams fell on
her face, so one of the swans flew
over her head and shaded her with
his broad wing.

Elsa thought she must be dreaming, it seemed so strange to be

carried so high in the air over the sea. By her side lay a branch of beautiful ripe berries, and a bundle of sweet roots. The youngest brother had gathered them for her, and she smiled her thanks to him. She knew it was the same brother who had hovered over her to shade her with his wings.

The whole day they flew through the air like a winged arrow, but they flew more slowly than usual for they had their sister to carry. The clouds began to gather and Elsa watched the sinking sun with fear, for the little rock in the ocean was not in sight. The swans seemed to be making great strokes with their wings. When the sun set, would they change to men, fall into the sea, and be drowned? Dark clouds came nearer, the wind blew wildly and the lightning flashed from the clouds.

When the sun had reached the edge of the sea, the swans darted down so swiftly that Elsa's head trembled. Soon she saw the rock just below them, but it seemed like a tiny speck. They sank quickly and at last she found herself on the rock with her brothers standing around her with their arms linked together. There was just enough room for them and not the tiniest space to spare. The waves dashed against the rock and covered them with spray. The lightning flashed and peal after peal of thunder rolled. But the sister and the brothers held fast each other's arms and watched for the rising sun.

VII

In the early morning the sea became calm and still, and at sunrise the swans flew away from the rock with Elsa.

They flew all day long again, and just before the sun sank in the west Elsa saw before her the blue mountains, the forests, the cities and palaces of the land of her new home. Long before it was dark she sat on a rock in front of a big cave. The floor was covered with delicate green creeping plants that looked like an embroidered carpet. "Now we shall expect to hear what you dream of tonight," said the youngest brother, as he showed his sister where she was to sleep.

"Oh, may I dream how to save you!" she replied. And thinking of this she fell asleep. She dreamed that a fairy came to meet her. She was radiant and beautiful and yet she was like the old woman who gave her the berries in the woods. "Your brothers can be released," said she, "if you have courage and perseverance. Do you see these stinging nettles? They grow around this cave. You must gather these even though they burn blisters on your hands. Break them to pieces with your hands and feet and make flax of them. With the flax you must spin and weave eleven coats with long sleeves. Throw these over the eleven swans and the spell will be broken. But from the moment you begin your task until it is finished, you must not speak. The first word that you utter will

185

undo all your work. Remember all I have told you." As the fairy finished speaking, she touched Elsa's hand with the nettle, and the pain woke her.

VIII

It was broad daylight, and close by Elsa's hand lay a nettle like the one she had seen in her dream. Then she went out of the cave to begin her work for her brothers. She groped in and out among the ugly nettles. They blistered her hands and arms, but she suffered gladly if she could only release her dear brothers. She crushed the nettles with her bare feet and twisted them into flax. At sunset her brothers returned and were frightened at finding her dumb. But when they saw her hands they understood what she was doing for them. The youngest brother cried over her and wherever his tears fell she felt no pain and the blisters vanished.

Elsa spent the whole night at work, for she could not rest till she had released her brothers. All the next day, while her brothers were away, she sat alone but never had the time flown so fast. One coat was already finished and she had begun the second, when she heard a hunter's horn. She was frightened and rushed into the cave. The sound came nearer and nearer, and a great dog came bounding towards her, then another and another. In a few minutes a hunter stood before the cave, and he was the king of the country. He came toward her for he had never seen a more beautiful maiden.

"How did you come here, my dear child?" he asked. Elsa shook her head. She dared not speak for her brothers were not released. She hid her hands under her apron, so that the king could not see how she suffered.

"I will take you to my mother," he said. "If you are as good as you are beautiful, she will dress you in silk and velvet, and I will place a golden crown on your head. You shall make your home in my mother's castle." Then he lifted her on his horse and galloped away over the mountains. When they reached the castle, the king led her into marble halls where fountains played, and where the walls and ceilings were covered with beautiful pictures.

But Elsa had no eyes for any of the wonderful sights, she only wept and sorrowed. Patiently she allowed the women to dress her in royal robes, to weave pearls in her hair, and draw soft gloves over her

blistered fingers. As she stood
before them in all her rich dress,
she looked so beautiful that the
court bowed low before her.

IX

Then the king declared he would
make her his bride, but the archbishop shook his head and whispered
that the fair young maiden was
only a witch who had blinded the
king's eyes and bewitched his heart.

The king refused to listen to him. He ordered the music to play, and the daintiest dishes to be served, and the loveliest maidens to wait upon Elsa.

Then she was led through wonderful gardens to the rooms that had been prepared for her, but nothing brought a smile to her lips and eyes. Last of all, her maidens opened the door into the room where she was to sleep. It had been made to look like the cave where the king had found her. On the floor lay the bundle of flax, and on the wall hung the coat which she had finished.

When Elsa saw these things so precious to her, a smile played about her lips, and the blood rushed back to her cheeks. She thought of her brothers and this made her happy again.

Very soon the church bells announced the king's marriage feast. The beautiful dumb girl was to be made queen of the country. The archbishop himself placed the crown on her head.

Elsa loved the kind, handsome king who did everything he could to make her happy. She longed to tell him about her brothers and how she was suffering to release them, but dumb she must stay till her task was finished. At night she crept away into her room and wove one coat after another. When she began the seventh, she found that all her flax was gone. The nettles she wanted grew near the cave and she knew that she must pick them herself. How could she get there? With a trembling heart she crept into the garden and through the streets to the cave.

Only one person saw her, but that was the archbishop. He was now sure that the queen was a witch and had bewitched the king and all the people. He told the king what he had seen. Tears rolled down the king's cheeks, and he went home with doubt in his heart. At night he pretended to sleep, and he saw Elsa get up and disappear into her own room. Day by day his face grew darker, Elsa saw it and did not understand the reason, but it made her tremble for her brothers. Her hot tears fell on the royal velvet and diamonds.

At last all the coats but one were

finished, and all the flax was gone. She had not a single nettle. Once more, and for the last time, she went to the cave to pick a few handfuls, and the king and the archbishop followed her. They saw her going from plant to plant with bleeding hands till even the king admitted that something must be wrong. "The people must condemn her," said the king, "I cannot."

Poor Elsa was quickly sentenced to be burned. Instead of the velvet and silk dresses, they gave her the coats that she had woven to cover her, and the bundle of nettles for a pillow, but they could have given her nothing more precious. She worked at her task with joy and prayed for help. Towards evening she heard the rustle of swan's wings close to her window. It was her youngest brother and she sobbed for joy, for her task was almost finished. The archbishop came to be with her during her last hours, as he had promised the king. But she shook her head, and by her looks begged him to leave her. She had only this one night to finish her task, or all her tears and sleepless nights would be wasted. The archbishop left her with bitter words against her, but Elsa knew she was innocent and took up her work with joy.

The little mice ran about the floor. They dragged the nettles to her feet, to help as well as they could. A thrush sat outside the grating of the window and sang the whole night long to keep up her courage.

It was still twilight, and an hour
before sunrise, when the eleven
brothers stood at the castle gate,
and begged to be taken to the king.
They were told they could not enter,
for the king was asleep and no one
dared waken him. They threatened
and pleaded till the guard appeared,
and the king himself came to see
what the noise meant. Just then

the sun rose and the eleven brothers
were seen no more, but eleven wild
swans flew away over the castle.

Then all the people came from the gates of the city to see the witch burned. An old horse drew the cart on which she sat.. They had dressed her in coarse sack cloth. Her lovely hair hung loose over her shoulders, her cheeks were pale, her lips moved silently, but her fingers still worked at the green flax. Even on the way to death, she would not give up her task. The ten coats lay at her feet, and she was working hard at the eleventh. The mob jeered her and said, "See the witch, how she mutters! Let us tear the coats into a thousand pieces."

They pressed towards her and would have destroyed the coats, but just then eleven wild swans flew down and perched on the cart.

Then they flapped their great wings and the crowd drew back in terror.

"It is a sign from heaven that she is innocent," whispered many of them, but they did not dare to say it aloud.

As the archbishop seized her by the hand, to lift her out of the cart, she threw the eleven coats over the swans, and they immediately became eleven handsome princes. But the youngest had a swan's wing, instead of an arm, for she had not finished the last sleeve of the coat.

"Now I may speak," she exclaimed, "I am innocent."

"Yes, she is innocent," said the eldest brother, and then he told all that had happened. While he spoke the air was filled with fragrance from millions of roses. The pile of twigs on which Elsa was to die had become a great hedge covered with roses. The king picked one of them and placed it in Elsa's hand. All the church bells rang of themselves, and the birds came in great troops. The brothers walked before the king and queen throwing roses in their path, and the people followed shouting for joy. No king or queen had ever before seen a bridal procession so grand and so beautiful.

WHERE THE FAIRIES LIVE

Where the fireflies flash and glow,
Where the apple blossoms blow,
In the land of Here and There,
In the land of Everywhere,
    Live the fairies.

Where the rainbow spans the blue,
With the sunbeams shining through,
In the land of Here and There,
In the land of Everywhere.
    Live the fairies.

Where the sparkling dewdrops shine,
On the morning-glory vine,
In the land of Here and There,
In the land of Everywhere,
    Live the fairies.

In the mountains, by the sea,
Where the honey tempts the bee,
In the land of Here and There,
In the land of Everywhere.
    Live the fairies.

See Teachers Manual, Page 45

THE RAINDROP

Once upon a time there lived away up in Cloudland some little water drops. Their home was one of the most beautiful white clouds that rolled over the blue sky.

By and by their cloud house seemed to get larger and larger, and darker and darker, and one tiny little water drop whispered to the other in a frightened way, "What's the matter? Our house seems so dark, and it's getting large, and just look at all the new vapor coming into it! Why, you're getting bigger, too, and oh dear, so am I. What can it all mean?"

Then the other little water drop laughed so hard it rolled over and over and almost fell out of the cloud window, but it answered, "Why, dear, we're gathering our forces together, and we're going to pour through the air and cut the biggest dash you ever heard of when we get down to the earth. Oh, it's the biggest fun!

"We fly through the air like fairies, and we can look down and see the people preparing for us. Some of them that are indoors run and shut the windows. Then we fly at the window panes and make music on them; and sometimes we dash right into the house before they can get it shut up tight, for you know there are millions and millions of us, so we divide the work. One little drop couldn't do anything that you could see. We always find a great many people out of doors. It is such fun to catch them. Some have forgotten their umbrellas, too, and that's the greatest fun of all.

"Often the wind goes with us. But I would rather he wouldn't, for he makes us appear so rough. The only creatures that really seem to enjoy being out when we're coming are ducks. You know water rolls right off a duck's back."

"But tell me as fast as you can how we divide work," said the first timid little water drop; "it must be almost time to start, for this cloud is packed so full I'm sure not another one can get in."

"Oh!" said the other, "we go wherever we're sent. Some of us fall right into the ocean and help push along great steamers, some of us fall into rivers and streams and do work there for a while, then move on to the ocean later, some of us sink into the poor parched earth and give it new life, some of us change into vapor again and come up to Cloudland, and some of us refresh the flowers. That is the sweetest work of all."

Just then the signal was given that two clouds were meeting. A rush, a flash, a crash, and the water drops were flying through the air, some to do great deeds, some to water the tiny little spring violets.

A SEASON

The goldenrod is yellow,
The corn is turning brown,
The trees in apple orchards
With fruit are bending down.

The gentian's bluest fringes
Are curling in the sun;
In dusty pods the milkweed
Its hidden silk has spun.

ST. GEORGE AND THE DRAGON

I

Once upon a time, when it was long, long ago, there was a good king, and he had a little daughter, Sabra, whom he loved better than his fields, or his gold, or anything which he had. For little Sabra was as fair as a lily, as sweet as a rose, and as kind and true as she was sweet.

But one day a terrible thing happened to the king. Down from the mountains, and straight through the gates of the city, came a raging dragon! It was black and horrible to look at, with eyes like two red coals and a mouth that breathed out fire. Its jaws were wide open, its claws were sharp, and it was as tall and huge as a forest tree.

Through the king's fields it raged, and it tore up, by the roots, the harvest of barley and rye and wheat. It killed the cattle and uprooted the grape vines. It lay in wait by the river bank in the tall reeds, and no one in the whole kingdom was brave enough to kill it.

The king sent his nobles to beg the dragon to leave, but no, it would not, and this is the message the dragon sent to the king. "Each morning the king must send one of the fairest little girls in the whole kingdom and fasten her to an old oak tree by the bank of the river for me, the dragon, to devour at my pleasure. Unless the king does this, the farmer shall not go back to the fields, and there shall be no food in the land."

There was great grief in the kingdom. Each mother held her little girl more closely, lest she should be the first one to go, and there was great hunger in the city, for no one could plant or harvest the crops. But little Sabra still laughed and sang as joyously as ever.

"Father dear," she said, "let me be the first little girl to go. I know if the dragon has your little princess he will ask for no other child. I will go in their stead, father."

II

Then the people came crowding to the palace gates, begging the king not to send Sabra, for they all loved her as well as their own little ones, but still Sabra said, "I will go to the dragon."

At last the king's high priest said, "We will bring a mother pigeon into the palace yard, and set her free. If she flies north, or south, or west, Sabra shall not be given to the dragon. If she flies toward the east and the sunrise, Sabra shall go."

So they took a brooding pigeon from her nest, and set her free in the courtyard. She spread her white wings and circled about in the air, and then flew straight to the east! Poor, sweet little Sabra! They carried her out to the river bank and fastened her to the oak tree where the dragon would find her, that so she might save the other little girls. Then they went sorrowfully back to the city again.

But the pigeon flew on and on, through field and forest, until she

came to a brave knight riding through
the woods.   The knight was tired,
and his good horse, also, for they had
been in a far country and had fought
many brave battles.   He had stopped
to rest under a tree, that his horse

might drink at the spring. As he rested, the mother pigeon flew straight to his shoulder and began cooing softly in his ear.

"I wonder what she means," said the knight to himself, as the pigeon flew off a little way and then returned, cooing. At last he jumped upon his horse and followed the way the pigeon led.

III

Straight through field and forest the pigeon flew, until she brought the knight to the place where the Princess Sabra was fastened to the oak tree and the dragon close by ready to devour her.

The dragon's breath was so hot that it burned the knight, and the smoke from its nostrils blinded his eyes, but he was brave and strong.

He made a huge ball of the sticky pitch of the pine tree. He thrust the end of his spear through it, and he rode straight toward the dragon's angry jaws.

The dragon reached out its sharp claws for the knight, but he hurled the ball of pitch down its throat and it was not able to open its mouth again or use its poisonous fangs. Then the knight killed the dragon with his spear. He unfastened the little princess, lifted her to his saddle, and carried her home to her father once more.

Oh, there was great rejoicing in the kingdom! The people crowded the streets and strewed flowers all the way for the knight to ride over. The old king held little Sabra close to his heart, and she put her arms

about his neck and kissed him again and again. And the king said the knight should be called St. George, and he gave him a wonderful gold cross to wear upon his breast.

NOBILITY

True worth is in being, not seeming,
   In doing each day that goes by
Some little good, not in dreaming
   Of great things to do by and by.
For whatever men say in their blind-
        ness,
   And in spite of the fancies of youth,
There is nothing so kingly as kind-
        ness,
   And nothing so royal as truth.

Mabel Betsy Hill

THE LITTLE BROWN BOWL

I

Once there was a little brown bowl that stayed always in a great closet among other bowls.

There were big bowls and little bowls, bowls with beautiful gold bands, and bowls over whose sides clambered rosebuds so beautifully painted that they looked as if they were growing. There was a bowl that wore violets all around its brim, like a little girl wearing violets on her hat. And there was one broad, shallow bowl tinted with such colors as are in the sky when the sun is going down, and on this bowl was the prettiest little shepherdess! She wore a broad hat and a blue dress, and her blue eyes always smiled.

So they were all beautiful bowls except the little brown bowl, which could never be anything but a plain, thick little brown bowl without even a daisy to wear. She was so shy among the others that she did not often speak, but one day, when the maid who took care of the china set a pretty little pitcher so close to her that it touched, she gathered courage to ask why the shepherdess always smiled and why all the other bowls were taken out of the closet at times and then brought back again, but she was always left.

The little pitcher told the little brown bowl that the shepherdess smiled because she was happy; for every morning she was carried to the sunny breakfast-room where Clarita ate her bread and milk from the shepherdess bowl.

II

Then the little brown bowl grew bolder, and said, so loudly that everybody heard, "And why don't they come and get me sometimes, as they get the shepherdess bowl, and the violet bowl, and all the rest?"

And the little pitcher answered, kindly, "They have not needed you yet. Perhaps, some day, you may be needed. Then the maid will come and get you."

"And shall I see Clarita, then?" cried the little brown bowl, in great happiness. But before the little pitcher could answer, such a laugh arose from the mouths of all the other bowls that they rattled on the

219

closet shelves, and the maid cried, "How the wind blows!"

"Ah," cried the rosebud bowl, "you will always stay on the closet shelf! You are too ugly ever to be needed. Do you see the rosebuds on my sides? Clarita loves them. Once I sat for an hour on a little table and held bonbons for her."

"And I," cried the gold-banded bowl, "have been near her at dinner and held water where she dipped her rosy fingers." And the gold-banded bowl laughed scornfully. "She loves the beautiful things; she would never look at you."

"No, indeed," said the violet bowl. "I wonder that you were ever put here. Once, long ago, I was carried up to Clarita's own room and held violets for her."

"Yes, and you were upset," said the tall vase, "which shows that you were never meant to hold flowers."

III

Then the little brown bowl sat quite still. She knew, at last, why for so long she had been kept in the closet, never taken out, and never needed. If only she, too, could have been beautiful! And she wished she might go away and never come back, since she could never be loved and never be of any use.

She must have wished it aloud, for the shepherdess bowl to whom all the others listened, spoke to her quite gently, "Do not grieve, little brown bowl. Clarita loves beautiful things, but she loves useful things, too, and if she ever sees you she will love you. Only be patient and wait."

221

So the days came and went. Each morning the shepherdess bowl went away and came back looking brighter than before, and one by one the violet bowl and the rosebud bowl and the gold-banded bowl were taken out, and brought back—I am sorry to say, haughty and vain—and saying unkind things to the little brown bowl.

One morning the maid came in and hastily set the little pitcher down. And the little pitcher, who always heard what was going on, was quite breathless with eagerness.

It was Clarita's birthday, she said, and Clarita was six years old, and six beautiful hyacinths were lying by her place at the table; and Clarita, as soon as she saw them, would surely be looking for something to put them in.

"Oh, dear!" sighed the shepherdess bowl. "Perhaps if I were not so shallow she might take me. Think of the joy of holding Clarita's birthday flowers!"

"Are the hyacinths purple?" asked the violet bowl. "Indeed, with my lovely shape and color, I stand a good chance of being chosen."

"You, indeed!" cried the tall vase. "Not one of you is fit to hold flowers. One would as soon expect Clarita to choose that ugly, silent little brown bowl in the corner!"

IV

But no one answered, for just then the door swung open and the little brown bowl saw a little girl

with sunny hair, lovelier than she
had dreamed. Her lips wore a
a smile happier than that of the
shepherdess and her eyes were deep,
like pools of quiet water.

She held her flowers lovingly and
looked eagerly among the bowls,
seeking something, touched the

rosebud bowl, and then—the little brown bowl fairly trembled with joy, for Clarita was looking straight at her and saying, "Oh, here is the dearest little brown bowl, mamma, just right for my flowers. It is so deep, and so strong, and too heavy to upset. Why did I never find you before, little brown bowl? You shall hold flowers for me all summer!"

Long days afterward the little brown bowl, filled as she always was now with flowers, stood on Clarita's breakfast-table, close to the shepherdess bowl.

"Dear shepherdess bowl," she whispered, "I love you, because you were kind to me when I thought no one wanted me."

And the shepherdess bowl whispered back softly, "Did I not tell you that it was better to be able to hold beautiful things than to be beautiful outside?"

And the shepherdess smiled more brightly than ever.

Mabel Betsy Hill

THE OAK TREE AND THE LINDEN

I

There was once a good old couple who lived in a little cottage upon a hilltop. Baucis and Philemon were their names. Although they were very poor, they tended their bees, and pruned their grape vine, and milked their one cow, and were happy from morning till night. For they loved each other dearly, and they were ready to share whatever they had with any one in need.

At the foot of the hill lay a beautiful village, with pleasant roads, and rich pasture lands all about it. But it was full of wicked selfish people, who had no love in their hearts, and thought only of themselves.

One evening, as Baucis and
Philemon sat in their cottage door,
they saw two strangers coming
slowly up the hill. There was a
great noise of shouting, and the

barking of dogs from the village,
for the people were following the
strangers and jeering at them be-

cause they were footsore, and ragged, and weary.

"Let us go to meet them," cried old Baucis, "and ask them to share our supper and stay with us for the night."

So Baucis and Philemon brought the strangers, who were quite faint for food, to their cottage, and they spread before them all that they had, which was very little—a half a loaf of brown bread, a tiny bit of honey from their own hives, and a pitcher of milk. The pitcher was only partly full, and when Philemon had filled two bowls for the strangers, there was only a drop left.

II

The strangers ate as if they had never tasted anything so good, although the supper was very small.

"More of this delicious milk, Philemon!" cried one of the strangers, and as Baucis took the pitcher to drain the last drop into the bowl, a wonderful fountain of milk burst forth from the bottom of the pitcher, so that the more she poured the more there remained.

And it was so with the loaf, which stayed always the same size, although the two strangers cut slice after slice, praising Baucis for its sweetness and lightness. The honey grew the color of gold, and sweeter each minute, and the single, tiny bunch of grapes grew to a bunch of such size that the strangers were not able to eat it, and the grapes filled all the cottage with their wonderful fragrance.

"These are strange travelers!"

whispered the old couple to each other, "who are able to do such marvelous things."

That night Baucis and Philemon slept upon the floor, that the strangers might have their bed, and in the morning they went to the edge of the hill to see the strangers safely started on their homeward way.

"The villagers are thoughtless and rude," said Baucis. "I hope they may not torment you again, good sirs."

But the strangers smiled, and pointed to the foot of the hill. There was no village there. Where it had stood a blue lake rippled, covering the houses and the trees with its clear waters. Baucis and Philemon rubbed their eyes in wonder.

"People with no love in their hearts shall not live upon the earth," said the stranger. "As for you, my good people, we thank you, and whatever you wish for most, that shall be given you."

As they spoke, the strangers vanished from sight, like mist in the morning sky, and Baucis and Philemon turned to see that their tiny cottage had disappeared also, and in its place stood a tall, white marble palace, with a beautiful park all about.

III

So the old couple went in, and they lived in their palace a great, great while, taking good care of their wonderful pitcher. No one ever passed their door without having a drink from the bubbling

fountain of milk.   Baucis and Philemon were so happy doing good
deeds for others that they never

thought of wishing for anything for
themselves.

But after years and years had passed they grew very old.

"I wish we might never die, but could always stay together!" said Baucis, one day, to Philemon.

The next morning, where the tall marble palace had stood, there was nothing save a few stones with the moss growing over them. Philemon and Baucis were gone, but there on the hilltop stood two beautiful trees, an oak tree and a linden, with their branches all twined and twisted together.

"I am old Baucis!" whispered the oak.

"I am Philemon!" sighed the linden. And there they stand to-day, quite close to each other, and always ready to spread their leafy shade over every tired stranger who chances to climb the hill.

THE STORY OF PERSEPHONE

I

There was once a wonderful fairy called Ceres, who took care of all the harvests upon the earth. Not a kernel of corn nor a grain of wheat could ripen unless she touched it with her fingers. Not an orchard could blossom and bear fruit, not a flower could bloom in the fields, not a single, tiny blade of grass could sprout until Ceres rode by in her chariot and bade them grow. She wore a wreath of poppies upon her head, and she carried a torch in her hand to light the autumn fires. She was very busy from morning till night, taking care of the crops.

Now Ceres had one little daughter, Persephone. Ceres was obliged to leave Persephone alone a great deal, and she always told her that she must not stray far from home. In those days, when fairies were in the world, there were also other strange creatures; the dryads who lived in the oak trees, the naiads who lifted their dripping bodies from the streams, the fauns with feet like a goat and little horns upon their heads who gamboled about the woods, and the ugly old satyrs with horses' tails and monkey faces. So it was not safe for a little fairy child to be far from home.

Usually Persephone remembered, but one day she forgot. She had been sitting for a long time upon the door-sill, making daisy chains, but she had picked all the daisies in the garden, and she thought she would just go a little way outside for more. On and on through the field she went, until she saw, gleaming away off, at the end of a meadow, a great bush covered with bright red flowers.

II

"I must pick just one!" Cried Persephone, running over to the bush and tugging with all her might

at one of the blossoms. It was
very hard to pick it, and all at once,
as Persephone tugged and pulled,
there came a great crack in the
earth at the roots of the strange
bush. Wider and wider it grew,
and there came a sound of horse's
hoofs and the rumbling of wheels up
through the ground. Persephone
gave one last tug, but just as the
flower came off in her hand, the
hole in the earth grew larger and
deeper and deeper. The sound of
the wheels became louder and up
through the ground came a team of
coal-black horses drawing a chariot
of gold.

There was a man in the chariot,
wearing rich garments and a crown
of diamonds upon his head. Before
Persephone could run away he had

seized her and drawn her into the chariot, and was driving away with her, down through the bottomless hole in the earth and away from the fields and the daylight.

"Mother Ceres! Mother Ceres!" cried Persephone, and she struggled to pull herself away, but she could not succeed.

"Mother Ceres, come!" she called, but Ceres was a long way off and could not hear her.

"I am King Pluto," said the man in the chariot. "The gold, and the silver, and the diamonds, and all the precious things of the earth are mine. You shall have them all, Persephone, if you will only live with me in my palace. I am lonely, and I have wished for a little girl like you."

But Persephone only cried the louder, as she said, "Oh, no, no! I want my mother, and the flowers, and the sunshine!"

It grew very dark where they rode. They passed a still, black river and King Pluto said, "Let us drink, Persephone. The waters will make you so happy that you will forget your mother and the flowers." But Persephone would not drink.

They reached King Pluto's palace, at last, which was really very beautiful, lighted with diamond lamps, and having the long halls lined with every sort of precious gem. King Pluto ordered a great feast to be spread of sweets and preserves, and a golden goblet of the wonderful magic water, but Persephone would not eat or drink. From morning till night she wandered about the great palace, a lonely little girl who wanted her mother.

III

Now, some way or other, Mother Ceres had imagined that something was wrong. She hastened to finish her tasks, and came home to find the house empty, and Persephone gone! No one knew where the child was. Poor Ceres! She lighted her torch and started out to look up and down the world for Persephone.

Ceres never stopped to rest. Her garments were wet with the night dews, and her wreath of poppies withered and faded. At every cottage she stopped to ask of the peasants, and at every forest to inquire of the fairy folk if they had seen Persephone. One had heard a child crying, another had heard the sound of chariot wheels, but no one

had seen Persephone. On and on traveled Ceres, and the earth was in a most terrible way, for she neglected all the crops.

The farmers ploughed and planted, but no grain came up. The flower beds were empty. The cows and sheep starved, but there was no grass for them to eat. And Ceres cried, "There shall nothing grow upon the earth until my little girl comes home again!"

At last King Pluto heard of the terrible blight upon the earth. He was not such a wicked old king, after all, so he called Persephone to him, and said, "Should you like to go to your mother, child? You may go if you wish, but you must eat with me first. Here is a fresh pomegranate. Eat, Persephone!"

IV

Persephone, although she had been with King Pluto for six long months, had not eaten a mouthful of anything, but she was so happy at the thought of seeing her mother that she took the pomegranate from King Pluto and ate a part of it.

Then she rode with King Pluto to the earth again and started over the fields to Ceres. And as she went, all along the path where she stepped the brown fields that had seen no verdure for so many months blossomed into violets, and the waving grain arose, and the orchards bent low with fruit.

Poor Ceres was sitting on her doorstep holding her torch when, all at once it flickered, and then went out altogether.

"What is this?" she cried. "My torch must not go out until I find Persephone!"

But just then Persephone ran straight into her mother's arms.

"My child, did you eat with King Pluto?" asked Ceres, after she had

held Persephone close for a long time.

"Only just six pomegranate seeds, mother," said Persephone.

"Ah, Persephone," cried Ceres, "then, for each seed, you must spend one month of every year at King Pluto's palace, and I may have you only for the other six."

So, half the year, Persephone lived with her mother, and Ceres drove over the earth and bade the crops grow and flourish. For the other half Persephone went to King Pluto's palace to make him happy, but Ceres mourned at home for her little girl, and the flowers died, and the fields lay brown and sere.

And that is how the first winter came upon the earth, because Persephone went away, and Ceres bade the earth sleep and mourn. But that is, too, how the first springtime came, because Persephone came home, and the violets blossomed wherever she stepped.

RHOECUS

I

One day a young man was walking through a forest. His name was Rhoecus. As he walked along he saw an old tree just ready to fall. It was a fine old oak with broad branches and large limbs. Rhoecus felt sorry that such a fine tree should fall to the ground, so he carefully placed a large stick against it.

As he turned to go he heard a voice speak his name. "Rhoecus! Rhoecus!" He looked around, but could see no one. Again he heard it, "Rhoecus!" This time it was a little louder, almost like a breeze.

He turned again and looked about him. His eyes fell on the tree which he had just supported, and

247

there beside it stood a beautiful maiden. As he looked at her she said, "Rhoecus, I am the dryad of this tree. I can live only as long as the tree lives. You have made my life longer by supporting the tree. Ask what you will and I will give it to you."

Rhoecus was very happy and he thought he cared only to have this beautiful dyrad for his friend. She might make him kind and gentle. So he said, "Only be my friend and give me gentle eyes like yours."

"I give it, Rhoecus. Meet me here an hour before sunset."

As soon as she said this she disappeared, and Rhoecus could see only the old oak, and hear only the rustling of the breeze among the leaves.

Then he turned and went on his way through the forest. As he walked along the sky looked bluer, and he was so happy he felt that he could almost fly.

II

When he reached the town just

beyond the forest, he found some of his friends playing games. He joined in the games and did not notice how quickly the hours were flying. He became so interested that he even forgot about his promise.

After a while a bee came buzzing about his head but Rhoecus roughly pushed it away. Three times it came back, and each time he brushed it away. The third time he bruised its wing, and then it did not return. Rhoecus watched it as it flew through the window, and while looking, he saw a mountain away in the west. Behind it the sun was sinking out of sight.

Suddenly it came into his mind that he was to meet the dryad before sunset. He started to his feet and rushed away without a word.

Through the city and over the fields he ran until he reached the forest. Once more he heard his name called softly "Rhoecus!"

He looked for his friend, but he could see only the dark shadows of the old oak. Then he heard the voice again, and this time she said, "O Rhoecus, you shall never see me again, either by day or night. I sent the bee as a messenger to tell you to come, but you brushed him away with a broken wing. We dryads can be seen only by gentle eyes, and he who is unkind to the smallest flower, bird or bee, can never look at us again. Farewell!"

Rhoecus was so sorry to hear this that he cried out, "O dryad, forgive me this once, and I shall never need to be forgiven again!"

But she only answered, "It will do no good; I cannot make you gentle. Farewell!"

Rhoecus was left alone.